C000049514

MAKING THE GRADE · *P*REPARATORY G...

EASY POPULAR PIECES FOR YOUNG PIANISTS. SELECTED AND ARRANGED BY LYNDA FRITH

Exclusive distributors:
Music Sales Limited
Newmarket Road, Bury St. Edmunds, Suffolk IP33 3YB.
This book © Copyright 1991 Chester Music
ISBN 0.7119.2525.9
Order No. CH59246
Cover designed by Pemberton & Whitefoord.
Typeset by Capital Setters Limited.
Printed in the United Kingdom by
Caligraving Ltd. Thetford, Norfolk.

WARNING: The photocopying of any pages of this publication is illegal.
If copies are made in breach of copyright, the Publishers will,
where possible, sue for damages.

To Mrs HARE
Please can you try to
order the next book in the
series from here,
Thank you

WALDEN MUSIC
21A HIGH STREET
SAFFRON WALDEN
ESSEX CB10 1AT
TEL / FAX: 01799 516919

Chester Music

(A division of Music Sales Limited)
8/9 Frith Street, London W1V 5TZ.

INTRODUCTION

This collection of 25 popular tunes has been carefully arranged and graded to provide attractive teaching repertoire for young pianists. New concepts and techniques are introduced progressively, and the familiarity of the material will stimulate pupils' enthusiasm and encourage their practice. The standard of the pieces progresses from beginner to Associated Board Preparatory Grade.

CONTENTS

ODE TO JOY

by Ludwig van Beethoven

This famous tune is played by the right hand only.

Remember to play on the tips of your fingers.

© Copyright 1991 Chester Music Limited, 8/9 Frith Street, London W1.
All Rights Reserved. International Copyright Secured.

LITTLE BROWN JUG

Traditional

The left hand begins this piece, but be sure to have
your right hand ready to play before you start.

watch for your hand shape

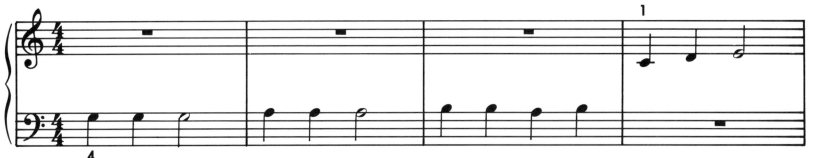

Keep a good steady counting going all the time.

© Copyright 1991 Chester Music Limited, 8/9 Frith Street, London W1.
All Rights Reserved. International Copyright Secured.

MY OLD MAN'S A DUSTMAN

by J.P. Long, E. Mayne & A. Le Fre

There are a lot of repeated notes here, so you will need to count very carefully.

count carefully

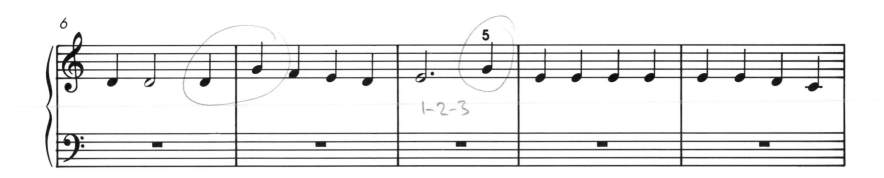

© Copyright 1922 Lawrence Wright Music Company Limited, London W1 for the World.
All Rights Reserved. International Copyright Secured.

TRUMPET VOLUNTARY

by Jeremiah Clarke

18th September

Allegro

make the hammers work ✗ Have your right hand ready before you start, and play loudly and firmly like a trumpet.

legs

© Copyright 1991 Chester Music Limited, 8/9 Frith Street, London W1.
All Rights Reserved. International Copyright Secured.

TWINKLE TWINKLE LITTLE STAR

Nursery Rhyme

When you have learned to play this piece, why not try playing it an octave higher?

25th September

don't book

© Copyright 1991 Chester Music Limited, 8/9 Frith Street, London W1.
All Rights Reserved. International Copyright Secured.

KUM BA YAH

Folk Song

This piece comes from Africa. It is the tune of a prayer,
so try to play it quietly and smoothly.

firmer fingers

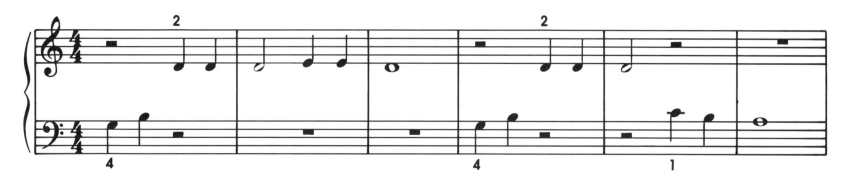

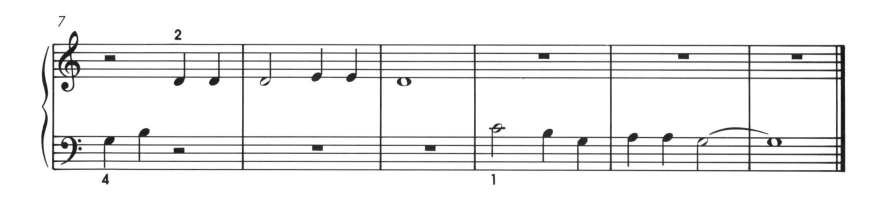

© Copyright 1991 Chester Music Limited, 8/9 Frith Street, London W1.
All Rights Reserved. International Copyright Secured.

I'D LIKE TO TEACH THE WORLD TO SING

by Roger Cook, Roger Greenaway, Billy Backer & Billy Davis

Notice the repeat sign [𝄇]. Remember to jump over
the first time bar [1.] when you play the repeat.

2nd October

✓

stronger finger work needed for a good clear note

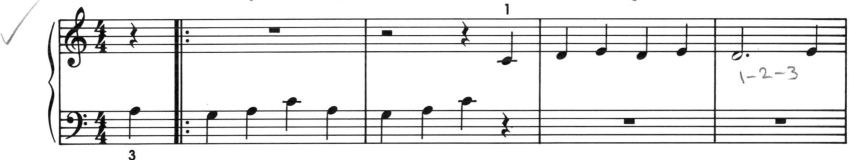

1-2-3

3

don't rush!

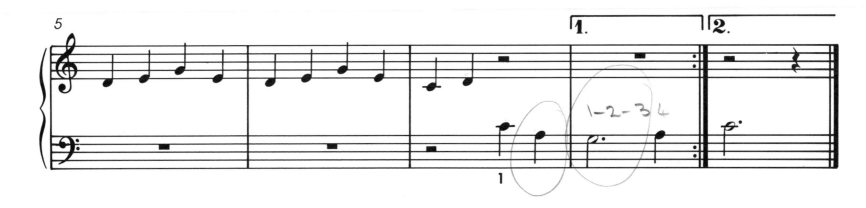

1-2-3 4

© Copyright 1971 by The Coca Cola Company, © Copyright assigned to Shada Music Incorporated, USA. Rights assigned 1971 for
the UK and Eire to Cookaway Music Limited, London W1. All Rights Reserved. International Copyright Secured.

HUMORESQUE

by Antonin Dvořák

This famous piece should be played smoothly and quite fast,
so you will have to count quickly as well.

Mouse house

Keep your fingers curled — hands well over the keys

count carefully

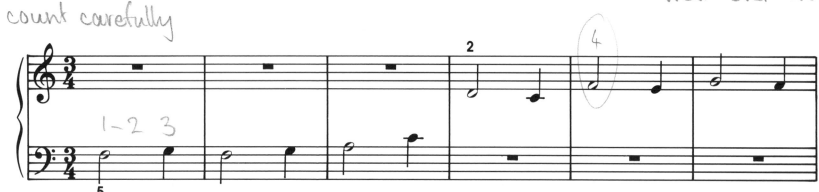

1 - 2 3

steady pace

10

9th October. a good start!

© Copyright 1991 Chester Music Limited, 8/9 Frith Street, London W1.
All Rights Reserved. International Copyright Secured.

p

tied notes

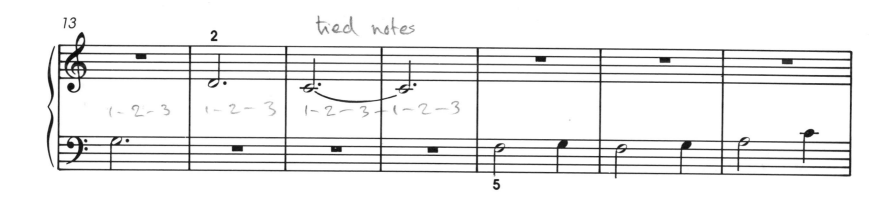

Keep counting carefully

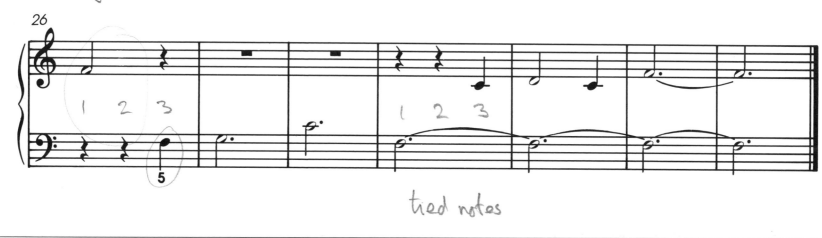

tied notes

good try

11

MY EYES ARE DIM

by Elton Box, Desmond Cox & Bert Reed

This tune has some quavers in it, and starts on the fourth beat of the bar.

Count aloud and clap the rhythm before you try to play it.

12

© Copyright 1940 for the World by Boosey & Hawkes Music Publishers Limited. Used by permission.
All Rights Reserved. International Copyright Secured.

WHAT SHALL WE DO
WITH THE DRUNKEN SAILOR?

Traditional

Before you try to play the piece practise the first bar

several times, with a relaxed wrist and clear rhythm.

✳ Notice the key signature – all the Fs are sharp.

16th October

Hand shape

check
your hand
position

good try –
well done!

careful counting

hands well over – bendy fingers

Relax
your
wrists

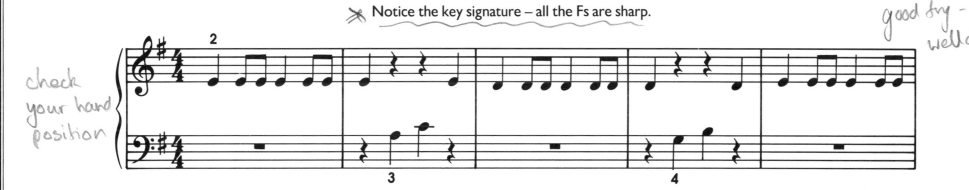

13

© Copyright 1991 Chester Music Limited, 8/9 Frith Street, London W1.
All Rights Reserved. International Copyright Secured.

THE BARE NECESSITIES

by Terry Gilkyson

There are two places, marked by *, where both hands have a rest at the same time.

Remember to count for these rests just as carefully as you count for the notes.

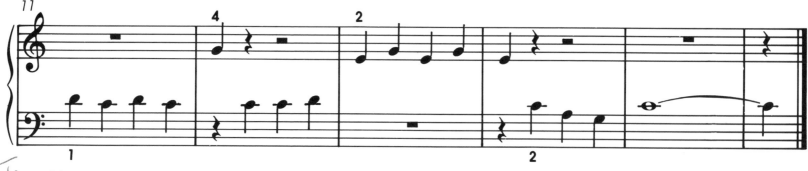

© Copyright 1964 by Wonderland Music Company Incorporated. This arrangement © Copyright 1991 by Wonderland Music Company Incorporated.
Used by Music Sales Limited, 8/9 Frith Street, London W1 with permission. All Rights Reserved. International Copyright Secured.

TOP OF THE WORLD

by Richard Carpenter

read this { Rests in both hands again. Look out for the F sharp in bar 10, and remember that the F on the fourth beat will be sharp as well.

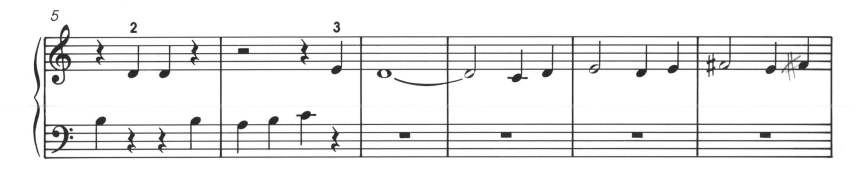

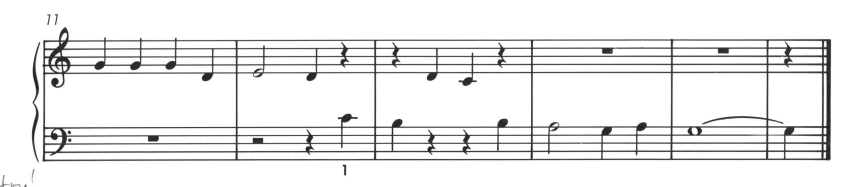

good try! ✓

© Copyright 1972 by Almo Music Corporation/Hammer and Nails Music, USA. All rights for the British Commonwealth (excluding Canada & Australasia) and the Republic of Eire controlled by Rondor Music (London) Limited, 10a Parsons Green, London SW6. All Rights Reserved. International Copyright Secured.

HI DE HI HOLIDAY ROCK

by Jimmy Perry

The key signature is B flat, which means the piece is in the key

of F and all the Bs will be flat.

Look out too for the E flat in the right hand and some A flats in the left.

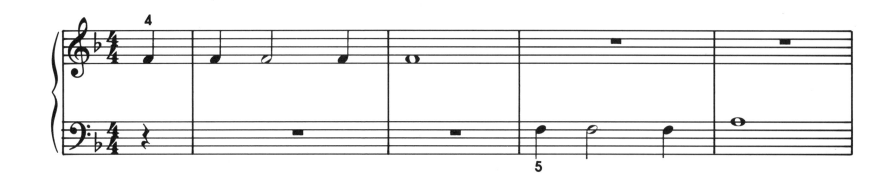

16

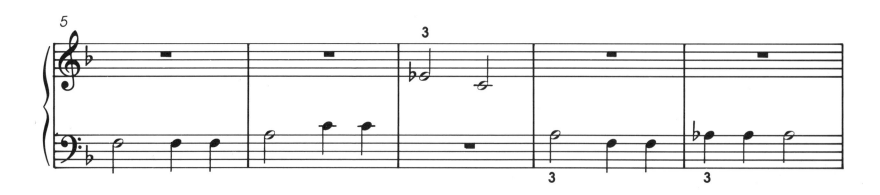

© Copyright 1981 Veronica Music Limited, 8/9 Frith Street, London W1.
All Rights Reserved. International Copyright Secured.

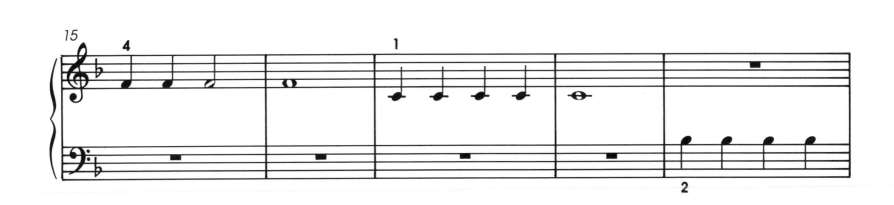

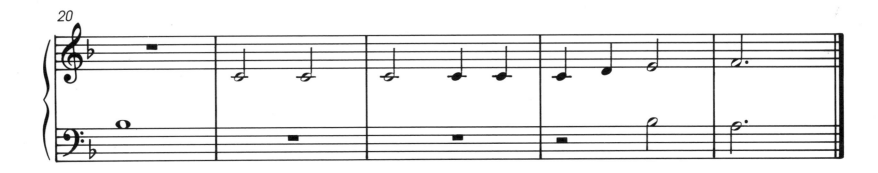

17

BIRDIE SONG

by Werner Thomas & Terry Rendall

Make the quavers clear and even. Remember that all the Fs are sharp, and make sure
you skip over the first time bars when you play the repeat.

© Copyright 1973 Intervox Music, Pierstraat 322 2550 Kontich, Belgium. All rights for the British Isles, Colonies and Republic of Ireland
controlled by The Valentine Music Group, 7 Garrick Street, London WC2. All Rights Reserved. International Copyright Secured.

EIGHT DAYS A WEEK

by John Lennon & Paul McCartney

Here the right hand starts in a new position, with the thumb on E instead of Middle C.

Notice the letters '*mf*' at the beginning. What do they tell you?

© Copyright 1964 Northern Songs, under licence to EMI Songs Limited, 127 Charing Cross Road, London WC2.
All Rights Reserved. International Copyright Secured.

SUPERCALIFRAGILISTICEXPIALIDOCIOUS

by Richard M. Sherman & Robert B. Sherman

In the left hand the little finger starts on the C an octave below Middle C.

At * the right hand has to move up to another position.

Practise this move before you begin the piece.

20

© Copyright 1963 Wonderland Music Company Incorporated. This arrangement 1991 Wonderland Music Company Incorporated.
Used by Music Sales Limited, 8/9 Frith Street, London W1 with permission. All Rights Reserved. International Copyright Secured.

FERRY 'CROSS THE MERSEY

by Gerard Marsden

This piece is about a famous ferry in Liverpool. Play it fairly quietly (**mp**).
Be careful to count through the minim rests in the right hand.

26th February

take note.

tied notes

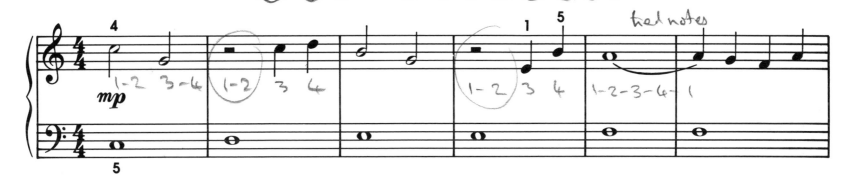

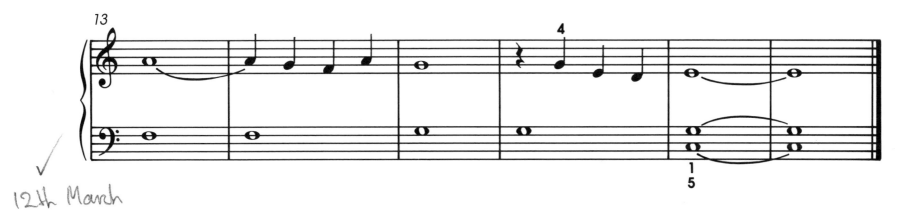

12th March

21

© Copyright 1964 Pacer Music Limited, Rights assigned 1976 Dick James Music Limited, Chancellors House, Chancellors Road, London W6.
All Rights Reserved. International Copyright Secured.

POSTMAN PAT

by Brian Daly

In bar four there is a special symbol 𝄐. This is called a pause sign,

and tells you to hold the note under the pause for a little extra time.

Notice the phrase marks (slurs) in the right hand.

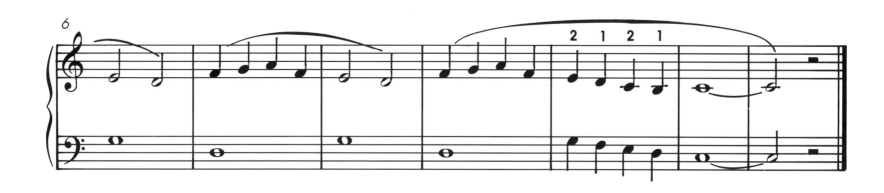

22

© Copyright 1982 Post Music, London SW15.
All Rights Reserved. International Copyright Secured.

WE ALL STAND TOGETHER

by Paul McCartney

The word 'Gently' appears at the beginning of the piece. Keep this in mind as you play, and notice the signs —— and —— , which tell you to get louder then softer.

26th March
good try! — now both hands!

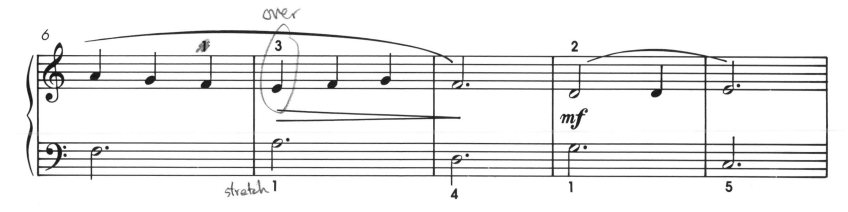

© Copyright 1984 MPL Communication Limited, 1 Soho Square, London W1.
All Rights Reserved. International Copyright Secured.

23

WHILE SHEPHERDS WATCHED

Traditional

In this well-known carol the right hand has to play the note B below Middle C.
Practise the bar where this happens (bar six) carefully, putting the
second finger over the top of the thumb as marked.

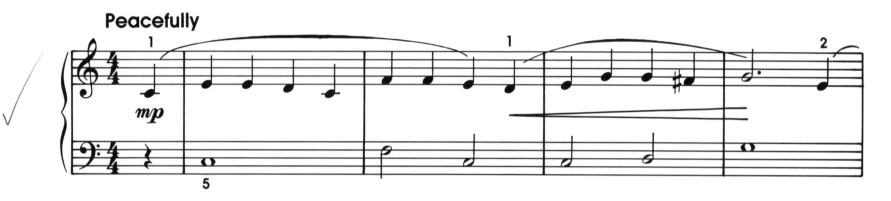

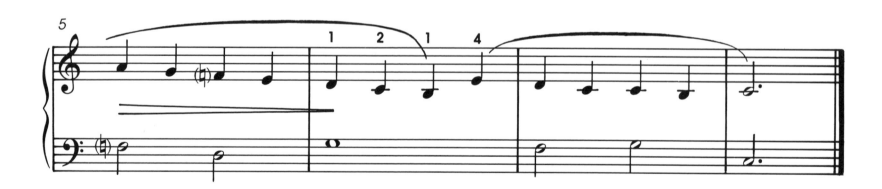

24

© Copyright 1991 Chester Music Limited, 8/9 Frith Street, London W1.
All Rights Reserved. International Copyright Secured.

HEY JUDE

by John Lennon & Paul McCartney

At the end of bar four in the right hand, be sure to pass the thumb under
the second finger to take the hand up to the new position.
Bar 10 is a bit tricky, and worth special practice.

1st April

watch out for the tied notes

Not too fast

*7th May
good
counting*

© Copyright 1968 Northern Songs, under licence to EMI Songs Limited, 127 Charing Cross Road, London WC2.
All Rights Reserved. International Copyright Secured.

7th May

THE BEAR WENT OVER THE MOUNTAIN

American Folk Song

You may know this tune as 'For He's A Jolly Good Fellow'.

Make the phrasing very clear, and look out for the pause sign near the end.

Quite brightly

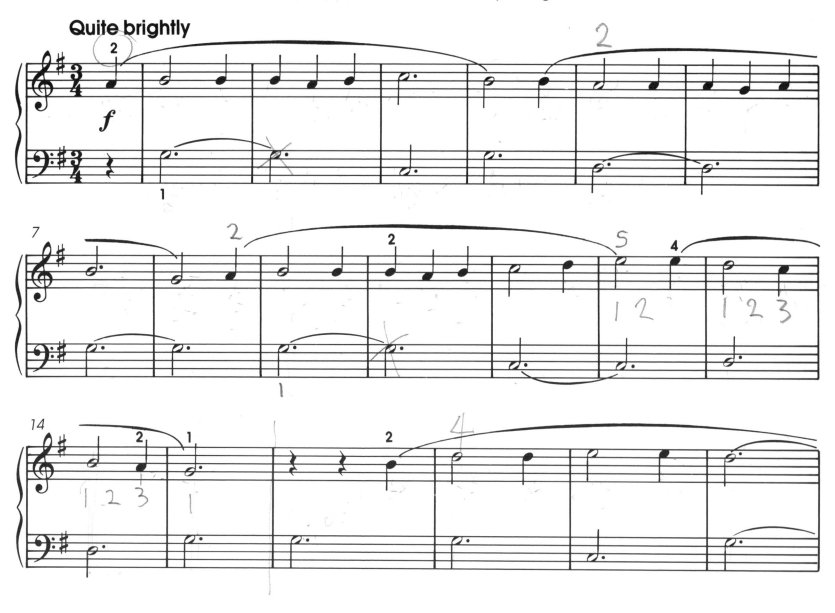

© Copyright 1991 Chester Music Limited, 8/9 Frith Street, London W1.
All Rights Reserved. International Copyright Secured.

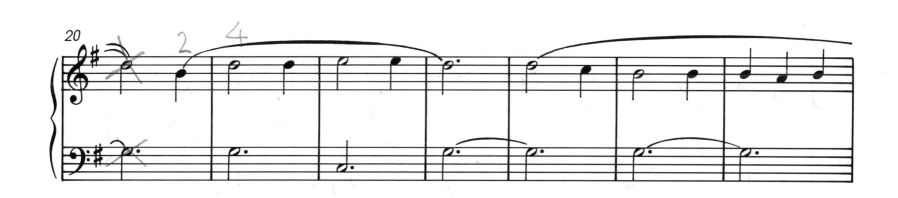

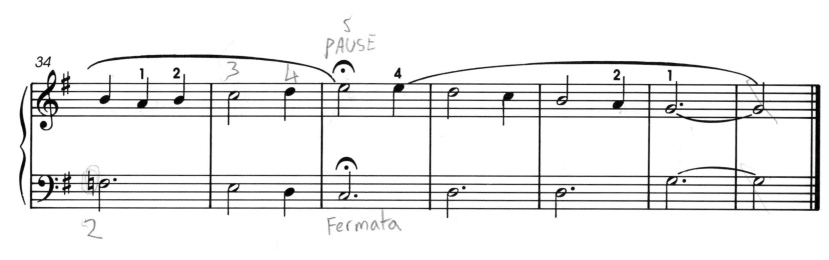

BLOWIN' IN THE WIND

by Bob Dylan

Look at bar three. After playing G with the right hand 4th finger you have to
stretch the 3rd finger down to E, missing out the F.
This happens in three places in the piece, marked by the sign ⌐.

12th Nov.

finger tips!

wrist up – level with arm

dotted minim

♩. = 3 beats

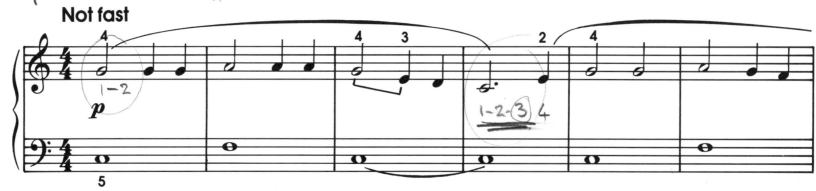

28

© Copyright 1962 by M. Witmark & Sons, USA. Warner Chappell Music Limited, 129 Park Street, London W1.
All Rights Reserved. International Copyright Secured.

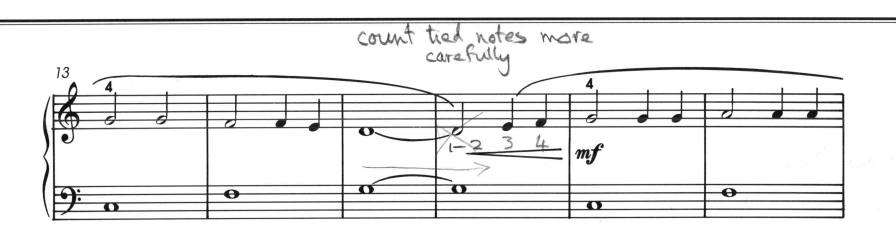

count tied notes more
carefully

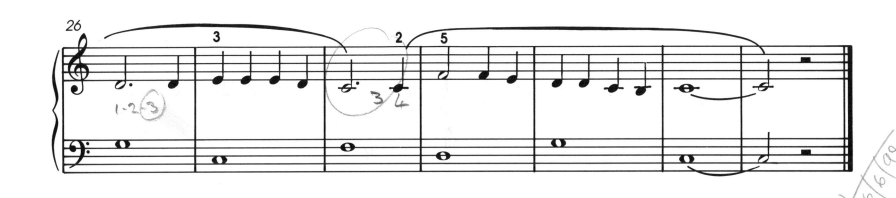

26/6/98

Y VIVA ESPANA

by Leo Caerts

This is a very happy tune about holidays in Spain.

Try to make it sound lively and full of fun

– but watch out for the E flats at the end.

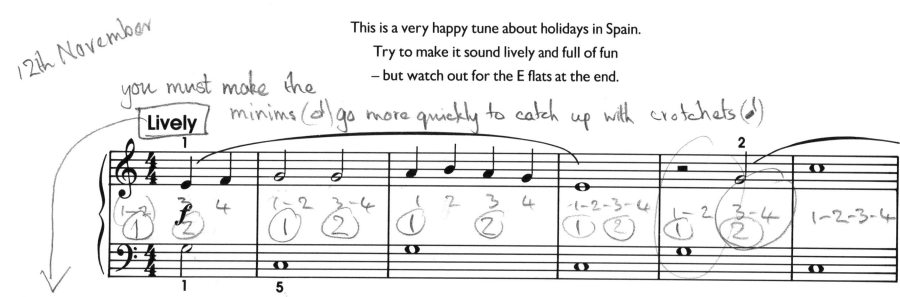

© Copyright 1973 by Editions Basart, Belgium. Intersong Music Limited, 129 Park Street, London W1.
All Rights Reserved. International Copyright Secured.

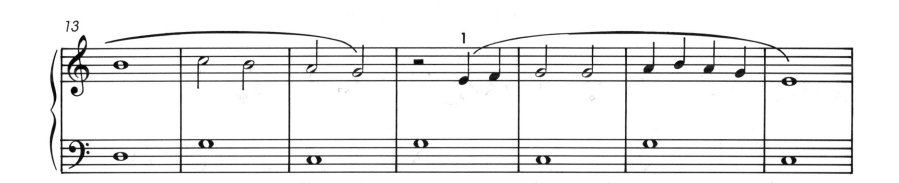

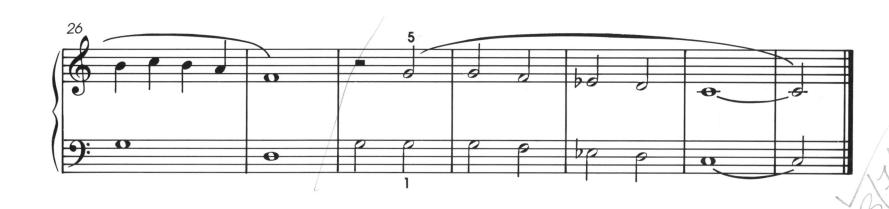

UPTOWN GIRL

by Billy Joel

The right hand has a lot of quavers which go quite quickly, so it would be a good
idea to practise the right hand on its own until you are really sure of it.

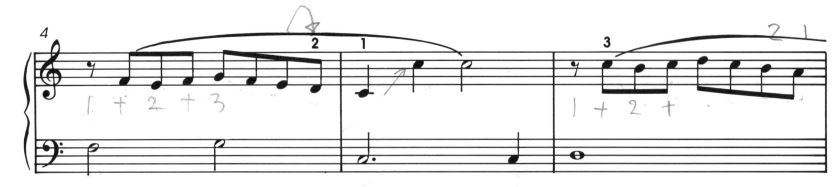

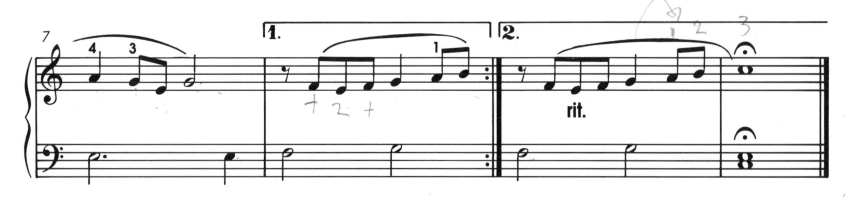

© Copyright 1983 Joelsongs, USA. All rights administered by SBK Songs Limited, 127 Charing Cross Road, London WC2.
All Rights Reserved. International Copyright Secured.